This book is f[...]
want to become a Jum[...]
become a better Jump[...]
jumpers and non-airbo[...] [...]

MW00628042

Being a Jumpmaster is an awesome responsibility that should not be taken lightly. Every Soldier you inspect and put out of an aircraft, that Soldier's life is in your hands. It is your duty to be the best Jumpmaster that you can possibly be.

This book will provide you key tips and tricks on how to become a Jumpmaster and once you are a Jumpmaster, this book will teach you tricks on how to be the best at what you do.

For those of you up to the challenge, I salute you.

My credentials. I have 93-recorded jumps and over 30+ Jumpmaster duties. I have served 6 years in the 82d Airborne Division (almost 2 years as an S3) and have successfully helped train over 20 NCO's and officers to pass Jumpmaster school as first time go's. Jumpmastering is a way of life for me.

Author's Disclaimer: Unfortunately, I have to write this next statement. Though I have safely used and followed these tips and tricks for 6 years, due to the type of society we live in today I have to state that the author cannot be held liable nor responsible for any injuries or deaths caused by the use of any of these tips, tricks, or ideas. Also, always consult the ASOP before any airborne operation.

SPECIAL THANKS

to

LTC Tracy, SGM Burney, SSG Tate, SGT Matt, SGT Liles, and SGT Eunice

for their Jumpmaster leadership to Soldiers

to

LTG(R) Kind and COL(R) Taylor

for inspiring me to become a Jumpmaster and not be another "dirty, nasty leg"

to

CPT Dennard who helped with pictures

to

CPT Creson and Melissa Creson

for their friendship, help with pictures, and editing

to

my Mom, friends, and family who have supported me in my goals, my pursuit for excellence, and in raising my daughter

and to

Kathleen, my daughter, who learned the jump commands at age 5 by the way, I love you and am proud of you for just being you.

TABLE OF CONTENTS

FOR THE PRETEST

There are 10 critical items you need to learn/know/do before taking the pretest.

1. First of all, you must know the proper nomenclature for all the airborne items of equipment. The nomenclature may be found in the AAS Jumpmaster Student Study Guide located at www.bragg.army.mil/aas/. If you don't know proper nomenclature like the back of your hand, not only will Jumpmaster school be ten times harder, but you will also have a hard time communicating with other Jumpmasters and you will not inspire confidence in jumpers. The way I learned the terms was by saying each one over and over in my mind 5-10 times and then pointing to the item of equipment on the piece of paper. Other people make flash cards or write the terms down a few times. After I learned the terms and when I was on a jump, I would practice saying the terms and point to the real thing to get a better feel/recognition of the item.

2. Secondly, Practice, Practice, Practice. You must know how to properly rig your ALICE Pack and an M1950 Weapon's Case within 15 minutes or less with zero deficiencies. With practice you will see your rigging time decrease from 15 minutes or more to somewhere around 8-12 minutes. To be successful on test day, you need to consistently be able to rig your equipment without any errors in 12 minutes or less. I will tell you my step-by-step strategy for rigging at the end of these 10 pretest tips.

3. Third, your ALICE Pack must be squared away. Fill your ALICE Pack with 35 lbs or less of weight making absolutely sure

that the ALICE Pack looks well rounded/filled. Also, fill out the 3 bottom pouches on your ALICE Pack. You want your left, center, and right pouches to be bulging out. Use MREs, wet weather gear, etc. to fill out the pouches. These tips will not only help the H-Harness to fit better on your ALICE Pack, but will also make the appearance of your equipment look more professional on test day.

4. Fourth, show up early on test day and place your ALICE Pack in one of the 4 rows of 20 spaces across. If you count 20 across from the right and decide to make a 21st spot, you just went to the back of the line!

20 ← 4 3 2 1	Row 1
20	Row 2
20	Row 3
20	Row 4

5. Fifth, your HPT Lowering Line must be serviceable, fold easily like an accordion with no edges protruding out from the Retainer Flap, and look sharp and crisp. To get your HPT Lowering Line looking sharp and crisp, iron your HPT Lowering Line. Then, iron and starch the folds in your HPT Lowering Line. You want to layer (fold) your HPT Lowering Line just a little inside the edges of the Retainer Flap on the first layer. On the second layer, create the layer (fold) just a little farther in than the first. The third layer should look like the first. The fourth like the second and so on. See Figure 1-1. Not only does the starching and ironing make the HPT Lowering Line look better, it also lets you know where you need to fold the HPT Lowering Line every time. When not in use, always keep your HPT Lowering Line folded so it retains its shape! Note: Some people like to keep the folds even. That is fine if it works for you.

Figure 1-1

6. Sixth, practice folding your HPT Lowering Line on top of the M1950 Weapon's Case. This will make folding the HPT Lowering Line easier on test day when you are in the sawdust pit because you have already trained this way. Trust me, you don't want to fold the HPT Lowering Line in the sawdust and you don't want to learn how to fold it on the M1950 Weapon's Case for the first time on test day.

7. Seventh, practice rigging your equipment with 1" wide masking tape to tie down the free ends of your Equipment Retainer Straps and use retainer bands only to attach your HPT Lowering Line to the ALICE Pack frame. On test day, the Advanced Airborne School will provide you with the tape and retainer bands they want you to use. Most people rush to get these items when your rigging time starts and fight over each other to get tape and retainer bands wasting each other's precious time. Go to your equipment and start rigging. Once you get your ALICE Pack rigged, then go over to the tape/retainer band location. Note: Rip off 6x10" long strips of tape and place the tape strips on your BDU pant legs, grab 6-8 retainer bands, and then run back to your location. You are now

6

prepared to finish rigging your ALICE Pack and HPT Lowering Line. You will also have extra tape and retainer bands if you need them.

8. Eighth, train with the same equipment you take to the pretest. Keep your ALICE Pack filled to the same amount. Don't change anything. You know how the equipment is supposed to look.

9. Ninth, M1950 Weapon's Case inspection. Immediately inspect the M1950 Weapon's Case when it is issued to you. Get it, stand to the side, and inspect! If your M1950 Weapon's Case is not serviceable, turn it in and get another one. An unserviceable M1950 Weapon's Case is an automatic no-go! Note: While we are talking about the M1950 Weapon's Case, ensure you secure the Tab Thong with the Upper Tie Down Tape or the Lift Fastener, but never both.

10. Tenth, ensure your ACH or Ballistic Helmet has all new components and all pieces are assembled properly. Do not mix and match old equipment with new equipment. Have the Jumpmaster you respect the most inspect your helmet just to be safe.

Note: In the near future, the MOLLE may replace the ALICE Pack. Contact your Schools NCO to know what equipment you need for the Pretest. Also, anywhere ALICE Pack is written in this book, MOLLE can be substituted.

Proper rigging of the ALICE Pack with HPT Lowering Line and M1950 Weapon's Case for the Jumpmaster Pretest

Note: I am teaching and showing the ALICE Pack as all the steps are the same for the MOLLE. If you can rig an ALICE Pack, you can rig a MOLLE. It is much harder to teach the opposite way though as the MOLLE does not have all the pockets an ALICE Pack does. The AAS Jumpmaster Student Study Guide tells you how to specifically rig a MOLLE. Also, the rest of this chapter is written with the mindset that you have a basic understanding of how to rig your equipment and know proper nomenclature. If you don't, wait until you do.

Here is my system. I always lay out my equipment (ALICE Pack, M1950 Weapon's Case, HPT Lowering Line, and H-Harness) in <u>the same way every time</u> and I always rig my ALICE Pack and M1950 Weapon's Case <u>the same way every time</u>. Why? It creates a system so that: one, you don't forget to do something; two, it enables you to get into a steady rhythm and work faster; and three, you don't have to think about what to do next (eliminates the panic factor).

Layout:

First, I place my ALICE Pack on the ground with the ammo pouches facing to the ground and the kidney pad facing up. Then, I lay out the H-Harness about a foot away from the ALICE Pack. Next, I place each Female portion, Leg Strap Release Assembly next to each White Attaching Loop. I also place each Adjustable D-Ring Attaching Strap with the opening gate facing down and away from the harness and with each Triangle Link next to each White Attaching Loop (Figure 1-2). Unhitch the Release Handle from the Release Handle Assembly and place the Release Handle just before the Release Handle Cross Strap. Ensure the Release Handle Lanyard is not twisted. Open the Release Handle Cross Strap (Figure 1-2).

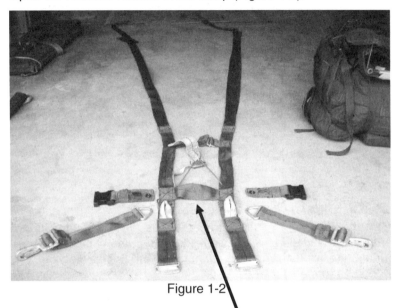

Figure 1-2

Tilted Open Release Handle Cross Strap

Now, set out the HPT Lowering Line about 3 feet away from the H-Harness and elongate the lowering line all the way.

Next, place the M1950 Weapon's Case about a foot away from the HPT Lowering Line and open the Retainer Flap. Place your mock weapon (2x4 with rock facing up) next to the open Retainer Flap (Figure 1-3).

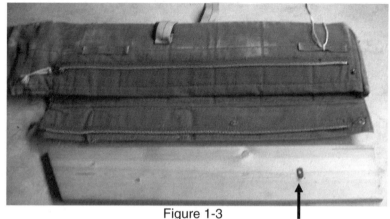

Figure 1-3

rock

Rigging:

1. Place Release Handle through Release Handle Cross Strap.
2. Place Triangle Link of Adjustable D-Ring Attaching Strap on top of the White Attaching Loop and pull the White Attaching Loop through the Triangle Link.
3. Place the Green Attaching Loop through the White Attaching Loop.
4. Place the Red Attaching Loop through the Green Attaching Loop.
5. Place the Female Portion, Leg Strap Release Assembly Grommet over the Red Attaching Loop and pull the Red Attaching Loop through the Grommet.
6. Route the Release Handle Cable through the Red Attaching Loop (above the grommet) and into the Webbing Retainer.
7. Repeat steps 2-6 on the other side. See Figure 1-4.

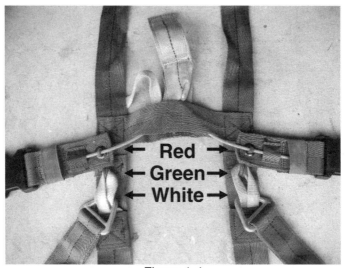

Figure 1-4

8. Flip the H-Harness over (upside down). Elongate all straps and ensure there are no twists.

9. Place ALICE Pack center pouch in-between Release Handle Cross Strap and Adjustable Cross Strap.

10. Pull one Friction Adapter under the ALICE Pack frame (Figure 1-5).

11. Grab the opposite Leg Strap near the top of the ALICE Pack frame, ensure there are no twists, and route it under the ALICE Pack frame and to the Friction Adapter. Form a bight with the excess webbing. Route the bight under the Floating Metal Bar of the Friction Adapter (Figure 1-6). Once you have pulled a few inches of the bight through the Friction Adapter, grab a portion of the webbing on the pulled through side and pull the rest of the

excess webbing all the way through the Friction Adapter (Figure 1-7).

Figure 1-5

Figure 1-6   Figure 1-7

12. Form another bight and route the equipment retainer strap over the Floating Metal Bar and through the Friction Adapter going the opposite direction as in Step 11. Keep the bight and tighten slightly (Figure 1-8).

Figure 1-8

13. Repeat steps 10-12 for the other side. When finished, your equipment retainer straps should make an X and you can see a loose bight from the Friction Adapters on each side. The loose bights are your Quick Releases (Figure 1-9).

Figure 1-9

14. Slightly turn the ALICE Pack over and ensure the center pouch is centered between the Release Handle Cross Strap and the Adjustable Cross Strap then tighten the Adjustable Cross Strap. Drop the ALICE Pack down.

15. Tighten both Friction Adapters that form the X in Step 13 and adjust the Quick Releases to 2-3 finger widths (Figure 1-9).

16. Run and get your 6 strips of approximately 10" long 1" wide masking tape and 6-8 retainer bands. Place the tape strips horizontally across each of your thighs and run back to your equipment. Note: 2x pieces of tape are extras. Use as needed.

17. S-fold the excess webbing from both Quick Releases in 2-3" sections and wrap each of them with a 10" long piece of 1" wide masking tape (Figure 1-10). DO NOT secure the excess webbing to the Quick Releases.

Figure 1-10

18. Tighten down both of the ALICE Pack shoulder carrying straps, S-fold the free running ends in 2" sections, and tape the free running ends with about 10" long pieces of 1" wide masking tape (Figure 1-10).

19. Rotate your ALICE Pack so that the top is on the ground. Grasp the webbing of the Male Portion, Leg Strap Release Assembly where it connects to the H-Harness and make a "dog ear" and pull it up the side of the ALICE Pack keeping out any twists. When your hand reaches the black Male Portion clip, grasp the clip in one hand and pull the free running end of the webbing down until the black Male Portion clip meets the Female Portion, Leg Strap Release Assembly. Ensure there are no twists in the webbing and then insert the Male Portion, Leg Strap Release Assembly into the Female Portion, Leg Strap Release Assembly. Tighten the newly formed Adjustable Leg Strap, S-fold the excess webbing and place the S-fold in the Webbing Retainer (Figure 1-11).

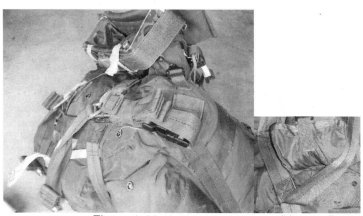

Figure 1-11   "dog ear"

20. Repeat Step 19 on the other side.

21. Move over to the HPT Lowering Line.

22. Set your HPT Lowering Line on top of the flat side of the M1950 Weapon's Case.

23. Begin S-folding the HPT Lowering Line. You want to layer (fold) your HPT Lowering Line just a little inside the edges of the Retainer Flap on the first layer. On the second layer, create the layer (fold) just a little farther in than the first. The third layer should look like the first. The fourth like the second and so on. Those nicely ironed creases are easy to spot aren't they? Once you are finished folding the HPT Lowering Line, set the Hook Tab portion of the Retainer Flap over the folded portion of the HPT Lowering Line. Note: Some people like to keep the folds of the HPT Lowering Line even. That is fine if it works for you.

24. Place the Pile Tab portion of the Retainer Flap over the Hook Tab ensuring that at least 50% of the Hook Tab is covered and check to make sure you have no edges protruding out of the Retainer Flap. Secure the HPT Lowering Line fringes.

25. Carry the HPT Lowering Line over to the ALICE Pack and route the Looped End, HPT Lowering Line either North-South or South-North over the X and then route the HPT Lowering Line through the Looped End, HPT Lowering Line forming a Girth hitch (Figure 1-12).

26. Tighten the Girth hitch and route the HPT Lowering Line over the left shoulder carrying strap (as you wear it) and secure the HPT Lowering Line to the ALICE Pack frame with 2 retainer bands. One retainer band will be above the intersecting metal frame brace on the ALICE Pack and one retainer band will be below it (Figure 1-12).

Figure 1-12

27. Ensure no S-folds are protruding outside the ends of the Retainer Flap of the HPT Lowering Line and that the Ejector Snap is facing toward the base of the ALICE Pack frame. At this time, I like to hook the Ejector Snap to the base of the ALICE Pack to provide a more professional appearance.

28. Move over to the M1950 Weapon's Case and slide your 2x4 with rock (or other object attached to it) into the M1950 Weapon's Case. Ensure the Forward Assist (rock) is at the top of the M1050 Weapon's Case and the muzzle (imaginary in this case) is facing to the bottom (Figure 1-3 on page 10).

29. Close the Closing Flap and run the Slide Fastener and Tab Thong (zipper) from bottom to top.

30. Secure the Tab Thong to the Lift Fastener **or** route the Upper Tie Down tape through the Tab Thong (Figures 1-13 and 1-14). NEVER both.

31. Form a bow tie on the leading edge of the M1950 Weapon's Case (Figures 1-13 and 1-14).

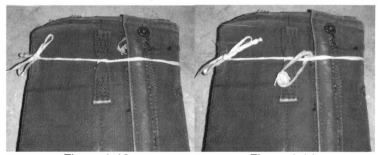

Figure 1-13
Tab Thong to Lift Fastener

Figure 1-14
Tab Thong to Upper Tie Down Tape

32. Flip the M1950 Weapon's Case over.

33. Route the Adjusting Strap through the Adjusting Strap Connector (both Metal Rings) and then route the Adjusting Strap over the Metal Ring closest to the Quick Release Link and under the Metal Ring farthest from the Quick Release Link.

34. Route the free running end of the Adjusting Strap in a Half hitch with the secured Adjusting Strap below the Adjusting Strap Connecter.

35. Route the Quick Release Link through the "V" Ring.

36. Attach the Quick Release Snap to the Quick Release Link. Ensure that the Opening Gate is facing away from the M1950 Weapon's Case!

37. Wrap the Lower Tie Down Tape around the M1950 Weapon's Case (Figure 1-15).

38. Inspect your Alice Pack.

39. When finished, place your ALICE Pack upside down and place the free running ends (Snap Connectors) of the Adjustable D-Ring Attaching Strap over the Kidney Pad (Figure 1-16).

Figure 1-15   Fig 1-15 Close Up

40. Place the M1950 Weapon's Case on top of the Alice Pack and you are done (Figure 1-17). Note: Steps 39 and 40 are optional, but they make your work look very professional.

Figure 1-16

Figure 1-17

Time Hacks: You should be able to rig the ALICE Pack in about 6-8 minutes, the Lowering Line and attaching it to the ALICE Pack in 1-2 minutes, and the M1950 Weapon's Case in 30 seconds - 1 minute 30 seconds.

BEFORE JUMPMASTER SCHOOL

There are 6 critical items you need to learn/know/do before going to Jumpmaster school.

1. Memorize Prejump completely! Let me say that again. Memorize Prejump completely. This will make Jumpmaster school a much more pleasant experience. Trying to learn to recite 4 pages verbatim in 4 nights is no fun. A few months before Jumpmaster school, learn a line or two or paragraph a night. Not only is it easier to learn this way, but you will also drill Prejump into your memory so that you will be able to say it anytime, anywhere without having to think about it. My trick was repeating a sentence 5-7 times then learning the next sentence. After learning the second sentence, I would say the first and second sentences together 2-3 times. Next, I would learn the third sentence, say all three sentences together and so on until I learned the paragraph.

2. Know your proper nomenclature forwards and backwards. You need to know what the instructor is talking about in class and knowing proper nomenclature will greatly help you when you start learning JMPI and calling out deficiencies. You do not have the luxury of time to be trying to think of what the item of equipment is when you are conducting JMPI. I am not kidding. When you see an item of equipment, the name should roll off of your tongue without you having to even think of the item.

3. Ensure your Ballistic Helmet or ACH has all new components and all pieces are assembled properly. Do not mix and match old equipment with new equipment. Have the Jumpmaster you

respect the most inspect your helmet just to be safe. It may have been awhile since you took the pretest. Trust me, you don't want to be ate up for the Black Hat.

4. Do not attempt to learn the JMPI sequence at all! Go into Jumpmaster school with an open mind and let the Black Hats teach you the sequence. Most people have trouble passing JMPI because they never master the JMPI sequence.

5. Invest in a good alarm clock. Do not be late for Jumpmaster school for any reason. Getting kicked out for being late to class wastes a badly needed Jumpmaster slot and makes your chain of command *real* happy with you.

6. Start reading the AAS Jumpmaster Student Study Guide so the information becomes familiar to you. Do not read anything about JMPI or PWAC.

Author's note: Just for laughs, below is a picture of my father in the harness, my daughter, and her dog on the reserve. Picture was taken when I was going through Jumpmaster school.

Chp 3
DURING JUMPMASTER SCHOOL

1. Learn the JMPI sequence. Don't worry about the guy next to you finishing before you even finish the front side of a jumper. He has most likely failed Jumpmaster school before for JMPI and will fail again for being a sequence violation. Learn the sequence! Speed can be taught later.

2. During the breaks while everyone else is talking and joking, rehearse JMPI shadowboxing and also rehearse JMPI shadowboxing <u>while calling off</u> the nomenclature <u>as you touch that imaginary item</u> of equipment. Also, if you have any questions, ask the Black Hat!

3. During Jumpmaster school, your sole focus is only on Jumpmaster school and nothing else. Do not go back to the office and don't get involved with other distracters.

4. AAS does not recommend you get a parachute and practice on your own with or without supervision. If you do not have a squared away Jumpmaster who knows his sequence to guide you, then I agree 100%. If you can get that squared away Jumpmaster and someone to wear the harness over the weekend or after Jumpmaster class, then I highly recommend this extra practice. I trained over twenty students this way and they were all first time go's! A squared away Jumpmaster who knows his JMPI sequence will teach you the tricks of how to move properly, identify where you are wasting time, and determine where you need to slow down a bit. The key here is that you have been learning the sequence in Step 1 above and

not been worrying about speed. Speed will come, but you must learn the sequence first or the speed is a waste of time.

5. Be smooth. The JMPI sequence should flow in a rhythm. It should not be jerky and you don't need to be rough with the jumper. Smoothness is the key. Not only does being smooth make the JMPI look more professional, you move quicker because you are not thinking about it, you are just doing it. So, learn the sequence and be smooth.

6. Never, ever, ever look for deficiencies when conducting JMPI! Learn the sequence! If you look for deficiencies, then your sequence goes to crap, you panic, and you find imaginary deficiencies. Learn the sequence. As you are practicing JMPI, you will learn what looks right. When you begin conducting JMPI with deficiencies, if you missed the deficiency, spend a few seconds looking at it so you know what wrong looks like and it will stand out to you the next time you see it in the circle, on test day, and in real life.

7. When a Black Hat corrects you, do exactly what the Black Hat tells you to do. If you need to slow down to remember, then slow down. If you need to ask for the Black Hat to show you again or explain differently, then respectfully ask.

8. Actions inside the aircraft. Every time you walk through a doorway, it is time to perform a door check. Practice makes perfect. I know you will drive everyone in your home crazy, but you won't be a PWAC failure either. When you can do PWAC on the ground like second nature, you will do just fine in the aircraft when the doors are open and your adrenaline is pumping.

9. Static Line trick. During Jumpmaster school, students spend too much time inspecting the Universal Static Line, because their flow is poor and they waste valuable time trying to cram the Universal Static Line in the Static Line Slack Retainer. Here is my trick. We will just focus on the back side. You have just finished the front side of the jumper and have the Universal Static Line in the proper hand raised above the jumper's shoulder. The Universal Static Line is in the "o" created by your thumb and forefinger. Keeping your eye on the Universal Static Line and your feet stationary, give the command, "Turn!" Keep your eyes on the Universal Static Line at the "o" created by your hand. As soon as the jumper stops turning, move the other hand (now the lead hand) with the forefinger pointing out or the forefinger and index finger pointing out and your thumb covering the two other fingers in the palm of your hand to just below the "o" you have made with your other hand (trail hand) (Figure 3-1). With your eyes following your lead hand, run your lead hand down the Universal Static Line to the first retainer band on the Outer Static Line Stow Bar (Figure 3-2). Then, quickly run your lead hand up the Universal Static Line to approximately the middle of the Universal Static Line between the Outer Static Line Stow Bar and the "o" you created with your trail hand. Bring your trail hand down and form a bight around your two fingers from the lead hand located at the midpoint (Figure 3-3). Remove your lead hand fingers from the bight and move the index finger of the lead hand to the bottom side of the Static Line Slack Retainer and push your index finger into the Static Line Slack Retainer and pull out to make room for the Universal Static Line to slide through (Figure 3-4). With the trail hand, push the bight through the Static Line Slack Retainer (behind your index finger). As you push the bight through the Static Line Slack Retainer with your trail hand, simultaneously pull the forefinger of the lead hand out

of the Static Line Slack Retainer to just below the Static Line Slack Retainer. As the bight of the Universal Static Line appears through the bottom of the Static Line Slack Retainer, put the forefinger of your lead hand through the bight, then pull down on the bight with the lead hand (Figure 3-5). Immediately after pulling the bight through the Static Line Slack Retainer, put your lead hand (now becomes the trail hand) with the Universal Static Line on top of the Pack Tray and begin inspecting the Universal Static Line at the first Inner Static Line Stow Bar (Figure 3-6). Keep your feet planted in one spot (or move one foot back and forth only) and follow the tracing of the Universal Static Line with your eyes no more than 6" away from your lead hand and the Universal Static Line. This simple trick will save you at least 8-10 seconds a jumper, so that is 24-30 seconds gained back on test day! Note: Your index finger should always reach the top of the Universal Static Line when you begin your trace. Note: Sometimes your finger will not stick through the Static Line Slack Retainer; in that case, while it is inside the Static Line Slack Retainer, push the Static Line Slack Retainer out so as to have more wiggle room to pass the Universal Static Line through.

Figure 3-1   Figure 3-2

Figure 3-3   Figure 3-4

Figure 3-5   Figure 3-6

Figures 3-7 to 3-10 show the proper tracing of the Universal
Static Line for inspection from the left Inner Static Line Stow Bar
to the right Inner Static Line Stow Bar and back to the left Inner
Static Line Stow Bar.

Figure 3-7   Figure 3-8

Figure 3-9   Figure 3-10

Chp 4
SAFETY DUTIES AND GENERAL JUMPMASTER
KNOWLEDGE

1. JMPI. When conducting JMPI and you find a major deficiency on a jumper, don't yell," Hey John, this guy has a cut Universal Static Line!" This will cause unnecessary panic among the jumpers. Handle the situation like this. Calmly call over another Jumpmaster or a Rigger to verify the deficiency if you are not sure. Then calmly tell the jumper, "You need to derig and get another parachute. I just found a major deficiency and we want you to have a safe jump." If the jumper seems a little scared, reassure the jumper that that is why you have Jumpmasters inspect jumpers' equipment to make sure it is safe and that is what you just did.

2. Adjustable Leg Straps (ALS). When exiting the left paratroop door, the right ALS is around the right leg and the left ALS is around the M1950 Weapon's Case only. When exiting the right paratroop door, the left ALS is around the left leg and M1950 Weapon's Case and the right leg is free (do not use right ALS).

3. Rolling D-bags. Once all the jumpers have exited the aircraft and you have gotten your thumbs up from the other Safety, it is time to start rolling up D-bags. This is a very simple and easy task if you know the tricks and a real pain in the butt if you don't.
    1. First thing you need to do is get all the D-bags in one spot, preferably next to a seat (Figure 4-1). I like to do this near the middle of the aircraft. I place my Aviator Kit Bags on the seat next to me now.
    2. Elongate the Universal Static Lines (Figure 4-2).
    3. Unhook the Universal Static Line Snap Hooks from the Anchor Line Cables and drop to the ground (Figure 4-5).

4. Take a seat next to the D-bags and grab one of the Universal Static Lines and start pulling the Universal Static Line Snap Hook towards you. If it does not come easily, grab a different Universal Static Line and repeat until one comes easily.

5. Quickly S-fold the Universal Static Line in approx 12" sections and place at the base of the D-bag (The base of the D-bag is where the Universal Static Line is attached to the D-bag (Figure 4-3).

6. Roll the D-bag base over the S-folded Universal Static Line like a sleeping bag (Figure 4-4).

Figure 4-1   Figure 4-2   Figure 4-3   Figure 4-4

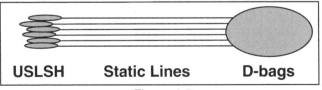

Figure 4-5

29

7. Place rolled D-bag in Aviator's kit bag.
8. Repeat. Note: Only 15 D-bags to an Aviator's Kit Bag. Also, if you feel like you are going to throw up, lie down flat on the seats or the floor and you won't feel like throwing up anymore. It is a tried and true trick that really works.

4. D-Bag retrieval when not using the Static Line Retrieval System. When pulling in D-bags, the Loadmaster should help you. Let him grab the top and then you grab as low to the aircraft floor as possible and pull in. Too many Safety's try to grab high. You need to grab low and let leverage work for you. It is a lot easier and a lot safer.

5. Aircraft Inspection. When inspecting the Aircraft there are a few steps you should follow for success:

1. Always bring a checklist and use it! (See Appendix B)
2. Always bring ¼ inch cotton webbing to run over the Anchor Line Cables from the forward portion of the aircraft to the aft portion to check for frays.
3. Always count the seats and seatbelts. Sometimes there are not enough of either one or the other or both.
4. As you count each seat, cross the seat belt over the seat and create an "X" (Figure 4-6). Reason is twofold- One, you confirm that the male and female portion of the seat belt is present and two, when you seat jumpers it is easy for you to hand the seatbelts (male portion, seatbelt from one seat and female portion, seatbelt from the seat next to it) to the jumpers and prevent mismatching of seatbelts. This sounds funny, but it is correct.

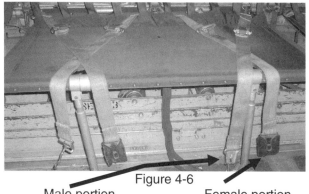

Figure 4-6

Male portion   Female portion

5. Always make sure there are earplugs present and if not, have the Air Force get some.

6. Seating Tip. When seating jumpers in aircraft other than the C-17, always seat the inboard jumper before the outboard jumper. Why? Because the outboard jumper always stands up before the inboard jumper. So, you will not only make the jumpers happier and have more confidence in you, but you have also reduced the chance for equipment to get caught on something.

7. Seating Tip. Always cram your jumpers into their seats when jumping a tight aircraft like the C-130. If you don't, jumpers will skip seats, you will run out of seating, jumpers will have seat belt problems, and you will have screwed up the load plan.

8. Water. Begin passing out water immediately after you get everyone seated.

9. Anchor Line Cables and Universal Static Lines. As a Safety, always count the Universal Static Lines hooked up to the Anchor Line Cables. Sometimes a jumper hooks up to the wrong Anchor Line Cable and now you have a safety hazard to correct.

10. Static Line inspection. When inspecting Universal Static Lines, always thoroughly inspect to see that the Universal Static Line is not misrouted and always tell the jumper "Hand your Static Line to the Safety!"

11. Static Line Control. As a Safety, never grab a static line with your hands as jumpers are exiting the aircraft. Form a knife cutting edge with your hands and sweep the static line to where it needs to go. Reason: If you grab the static line with your fist, it takes more time and your hand can get wrapped up in the static line.

12. Doors closed. When the paratroop door is closed after the last jumper has exited and thumbs ups are completed, begin rolling D-bags immediately.

13. Time for joking is on the ground. When you are in the air, it is all business. Lives are in your hands. It is ok to smile and be relaxed, but shaking the Anchor Line Cables and not paying attention to the mission at hand is another matter.

14. Paratroop door goes down. In the event a paratroop door will not open on an aircraft and the Primary Jumpmaster makes the decision to use the one good paratroop door to exit all the jumpers, the Safeties on the non-operational side of the aircraft need to immediately begin to fix all the Adjustable Leg Straps on the jumpers to match the leg strap requirements for the

paratroop door they are now exiting. Safeties also need to control the movement of jumpers over to the other side. When jumping a C-17, this is easy as there is plenty of room in the forward portion of the aircraft to move the jumpers in. When jumping a C-130 or a C-141, the ease of this operation depends on how the aircraft is configured. If there is an open area in the forward end of these aircraft to route the jumpers through, then do so. If there is no open area and you don't have time for one of the Safeties and a Loadmaster to make an open area, then you will have to rotate the jumpers over to the one good door at the aft (rear) end of the aircraft. Do not rotate those jumpers over from the bad paratroop door until you exit all the jumpers from the good side and close the paratroop door. Once the jumpers have transferred over in chalk order and outboard jumpers stay as outboard and inboard jumpers stay as inboard, the Safeties ensure all jumpers hook up to the appropriate Anchor Line Cable. All Safeties should help with the final checks of the Universal Static Lines and equipment after the appropriate jump commands have been given.

15. HPT Lowering Line for a single item of equipment (Combat Light jump). We have to modify the way we fold the HPT Lowering Line for a Combat Light jump because the Looped End, HPT Lowering Line will come out the same end as the Ejector Snap.

   1. You start folding the HPT Lowering Line the same.

   2. When you get to the last fold however, instead of going out on the opposite side away from the Looped End, HPT Lowering Line, you bring the Ejector Snap out the same end as the Looped End, HPT Lowering Line (Figure 4-7).

3. Fold the Hook Tab over the folds (Hook Tape over the end folds) and close the Retainer Flap ensuring that at lest 50% of Hook Tab is covered by the Retainer Flap.
4. Mate the Hook Tab on the Looped End, HPT Lowering Line and the Pile Tab of the Retainer Flap together.
5. Your HPT Lowering Line is ready (Figure 4-8).

Figure 4-7

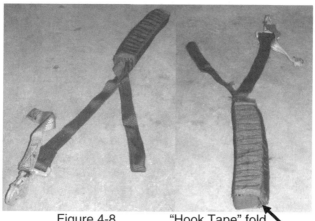

Figure 4-8   "Hook Tape" fold

16. M1950 Weapon's Case for a single item of equipment (Combat Light jump). I will only address the differences in rigging an M1950 Weapon's Case for a Combat Light jump here.

1. The Quick Release Link is NOT routed through the "V" Ring. The Quick Release Link is free by itself.
2. Attach the Quick Release Snap to the Quick Release Link ensuring that the Opening Gate of the Quick Release Snap is facing away from the M1950 Weapon's Case.
3. Attach the Looped End, HPT Lowering Line to the "V" Ring using a Girth hitch (Figure 4-9).
4. Place the bottom end of the HPT Lowering Line in the Lowering Line Stow Pocket.

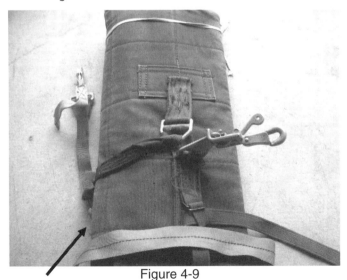

Figure 4-9
Lowering Line Stow Pocket

17. SARJE brief. SARJE is an acronym for Static line control, Activation of the reserve parachute, Red light procedures, Jump refusals, and Exiting procedures.

S- Static line control. For static line control, I like to only show the correct way with the elbow high, forming a bight at eye level (4" in the hand and 2" below), keeping eye-to-eye contact with the Safety, extending and locking the elbow, and handing the Universal Static Line to the Safety. Reason: If you show the wrong way, jumpers might remember that way instead.

A- Activation of the reserve parachute. If the doors are closed, the jumper alerts the Safeties and a Safety will replace the reserve. If the doors are open, immediately begin yelling, "RESERVE, RESERVE, RESERVE" and try to stomp it to the ground to contain it. If the reserve begins snaking to the door, again shout, "RESERVE, RESERVE, RESERVE" and anyone in front of it better get out of the aircraft before it or they will become padding for the jumper whose reserve activated. If the reserve activates in a C-130 while the doors are open and you are forward of the wheel well, shout, "RESERVE, RESERVE, RESERVE" and everyone in front of the wheel well and the person with the activated reserve need to immediately exit the aircraft.

R- Red light procedures. When the Jumpmaster sees the red light come on, he will immediately yell, "RED LIGHT, RED LIGHT, RED LIGHT." If you are in the paratroop door, the Jumpmaster will not stop you if you choose to exit. Note: The red light can come on for any reason, out of drop zone, low flying aircraft, problems with this aircraft, etc."

J- Jump refusal. I always tell the jumpers that if anyone is going to be a jump refusal, they need to do it while we are on the ground now so they won't screw all their buddies once we are in the air. That being said, once we are in the air and if you get up to the paratroop door and freeze for any reason, the Jumpmaster will yell to you, "GREEN LIGHT, GO; GREEN LIGHT, GO; GREEN LIGHT, GO!" If you choose not to exit at this time, the Jumpmaster will tell you, "You are a jump refusal and I am removing you from the paratroop door" while simultaneously putting his hands on the sides of the pack tray. The Jumpmaster will then remove you from the paratroop door. The Safety will then seat you on the ramp of the aircraft and give you a legal and a lawful order not to touch any of your equipment. Once the Safety returns to the paratroop door, the Jumpmaster will continue exiting jumpers if there is any green light left. Upon the completion of the exiting of the other jumpers, the Safety will then seat you down in a seat, seatbelt you in, unhook your Universal Static Line from the Anchor Line Cable, and secure the Universal Static Line Snap Hook to the top carrying handle of the reserve parachute. The Safety will again give you a legal and lawful order not to touch any of your equipment. Upon landing you will be JMPI'd by the DACO and every other Jumpmaster around and then you will be referred to your chain of command for UCMJ if no deficiencies in your equipment are found. Note: Jumpmasters never turn their back to the open paratroop door! The potential exists when you have a jump refusal so keep focused, take charge, use your safety, and be smart.

E- Exiting procedures. I will not address these as exiting procedures change fairly frequently.

Proper Stance and Static Line Control Procedures for the C-17 vs the C-130 and C-141 Aircraft

Fellow Jumpmasters, I am addressing a serious jumper safety issue that concerns me and the issue is where Safeties position themselves in a C-17 Globemaster.

Let me prep this. On the C-130 Hercules and C-141 Starlifter aircrafts, the Safety bisects the trail edge of the paratroop door and positions his/her body to face the paratroop door. The Safety turns his/her head to face the jumpers and secures the Universal Static Line with the lead hand and sweeps the Universal Static Line straight back and then places the trail hand in front of the Universal Static Line to maintain static line control (Figure 5-1).

Many jumpmasters are incorrectly applying this same standard to the C-17 Globemaster, thus greatly increasing the chance of a static line injury to the jumper. The correct standard based on the Advanced Airborne School Jumpmaster Course C-17 Globemaster POI issued in 1997 is: The Safety stands under the intermediate Anchor Line Cable facing towards the jumpers and secures the Universal Static Line with the inboard hand, transitions the Universal Static Line to the outboard hand and then guides the Universal Static Line to the top of the trail edge of the paratroop door with the outboard hand until the Universal Static Line is taught (firm). The Safety will remain facing towards the jumpers throughout the process. This will greatly reduce the chance of a jumper wrapping his/her arm over his/her own Universal Static Line or the Universal Static Line of the previous jumper (Figure 5-2).

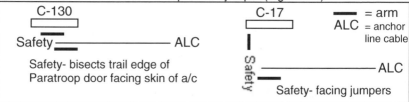

Figure 5-1   Figure 5-2

JUMPMASTER REHEARSAL

The Jumpmaster rehearsal is critical and I can't stress the importance of it enough. This is where the Jumpmaster team all gets on the same sheet of music and the Primary Jumpmaster ensures that the Jumpmaster team is competent. If any retraining needs to be done, it needs to be done here. When you are ate up in front of the jumpers, it is too late. As a Jumpmaster, it is your job to inspire confidence in your jumpers and the best way to do that is to appear confident, competent, and in control of the situation.

When I am a Primary Jumpmaster, I always have PowerPoint slide handouts (samples for you to use in Appendix A) that I go over with my team immediately after the air meeting. The slides cover how we will cover mock door training and loading of the aircraft. Why? I know it seems overboard, but it is not. Everyone on the Jumpmaster team needs to be on the same sheet of music and by covering the details of how you will work together as a team sets the whole operation up for success. Jumpers get their first impression of their Jumpmaster team during Prejump and mock door training. If you don't inspire confidence in the jumpers here, they will not have much confidence in you in the air. By the way, the Primary Jumpmaster should always give Prejump. Leaders lead from the front, right? I then rehearse with my team until I am comfortable in their abilities. Note: Ensure the Safeties know how to properly perform their Safety duties for a C-17 if you are jumping a C-17 or for a C-130/141 if jumping a C-130/141. See Chapter 5 for details. Note: Designate a Jumpmaster to check Adjustable Leg straps (ALS) at the ramp of the a/c when boarding the a/c to tighten loose ALS and to ensure ALS are routed properly.

Chp 7
MOCK DOOR TRAINING

Nothing looks more unprofessional and makes a Jumpmaster team look more jacked up than a poorly run mock door training. Safeties need to take control of the jumpers immediately upon the jumpers' arrival at the mock door (Left door Safeties will take control of their jumpers and right door Safeties will take control of their jumpers). The 8-step process is below.

1. Set up. See Appendix A, Charts A-1 and A-2. Using right door as an example. The right door Safety takes control of his jumpers and has his first inboard jumper with his equipment line up next to the skin of the mock up on the right side and the rest of the inboard jumpers follow in numerical order with their equipment. The first outboard jumper with his equipment lines up to the outside of the inboard jumper and the remaining outboard jumpers with their equipment line up in numerical order. This should take no more than a few minutes max.

2. Universal Static Line class and SARJE brief. Primary Jumpmaster has all the jumpers fall in around one of the paratroop doors with all first time jumpers up front. Safety that gives the static line class only shows the proper way of handing off the Universal Static Line. Why? If you show the wrong way, they may remember it instead of the correct way.

3. Set Up. Have all the jumpers fall back on their equipment. Then back them back up about a hundred feet or so while remaining in chalk order so that the last jumpers are poised to enter the aircraft from the aft (rear) position. Note: At this same time the other Safeties set apart 20 static lines on each door.

4. Move in to mock door. Have all the jumpers move into the mock door quickly, in chalk order, and take a seat. Do not hand out any static lines until jumpers are all seated! Safety then hands out the appropriate static lines to the first 20 jumpers. Note: Jumpers should ALWAYS hook up where they are seated. If you do this, you will never have too many jumpers on one anchor line cable no matter what.

5. 3 passes practice. Exit the first pass. After the first pass exits, the first pass Assistant Jumpmaster ensures the jumpers remain in numerical order far enough behind the aft end of the mock aircraft so that the other two passes can fit. Safeties for the second pass hand out the appropriate static lines and the second pass exits. Same steps apply for third pass.

6. 1 Pass. Have all jumpers get back inside aircraft. After all jumpers are seated, the Safety hands all the outboard static lines to the number 1 outboard jumper and all the inboard static lines (except one for the Jumpmaster) to the first inboard jumper. The jumpers take the last static line and pass on to the 2nd jumper and so on. After all static lines are handed out, conduct the mass exit.

7. Set up. Have all jumpers fall back in on their equipment.

8. The Safeties go to the rear of the formation (last inboard and last outboard) and has the formation follow him in reverse chalk order into the pack shed. Note: When the Safety seats the jumpers for his door, inboard sits on one side and outboard on the other side of the bench.

If you conduct Mock door training in this manner, you will look professional, inspire confidence in your jumpers, and you will save a lot of time.

Chp 8
WHAT EVERY JUMPER SHOULD KNOW

1. Landing. Proper landings are essential. We don't want any broken bones and if you follow my tip, you will never have to worry about that unless you land with one foot on a rock and another in a ditch. Nothing can protect you from that, but God. Ok, back to the tip. You already know to keep your eyes open on the horizon, feet and knees together, knees slightly bent, elbows tight into your sides, chin on your chest, and your toes pointed to the ground. That is good, but you need to take it two steps further. The first step is to put your elbows just below your breasts so you can't break them when you hit the ground and the second step is to lock your knees together as hard as you can and keep the rest of your body limp. Why? By locking your knees together, it will force you to do a proper PLF no matter what. Now, if you have a problem keeping your eyes focused on the horizon so you won't look down, reach for the ground, and break a leg, then close your eyes when you get to tree level and be prepared to make a good PLF because you will hit the ground 5-10 seconds before you think you will. I have never tried the eyes closed method, but I can speak from 93 recorded jumps worth of experience that by keeping my feet and knees together with my knees locked together, my elbows under my breasts, my toes pointed, and my eyes on the horizon, that I have never been injured on a landing and that is saying something.

2. Wind and Slipping. Slip/turn into the wind. What does that mean? What it means is whatever the direction the wind is blowing onto you in, reach up in that direction and grab the appropriate risers or pull down on the appropriate toggle depending on what type of parachute you are wearing. If you

remember this tip, you will always land into the wind and have a much softer landing than your buddy who slipped/turned in the wrong direction.

3. C-130/C-141 seats. When jumping a C-130/C-141 and it is time for you to put the seats up, don't panic. All you need to do is reach down the metal legs and about half an inch above the ground you will feel a ball detent. Press the ball detent in and lift up on the seat leg. Voila! The seat leg will be released. Once the other seat legs have been released by your fellow jumpers, you can secure the seat to the cargo netting with the seat strap.

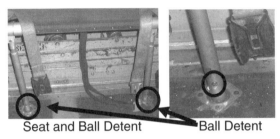

Seat and Ball Detent   Ball Detent

4. Adjustable Leg Straps tightening. After you have been JMPI'd by a Jumpmaster, the Jumpmaster will put on the appropriate Adjustable Leg Strap(s) based upon what door you are exiting. Keep the Adjustable Leg Strap(s) loose until you get to the base of the aircraft. Why? There is nothing worse than walking half a mile with your ALICE Pack / MOLLE banging the crap out of your shins for no good reason and then having the Adjustable Leg Straps loosen anyways, that's why! Instead, keep the Adjustable Leg Straps loose so you can lift up on the ALICE Pack / MOLLE and save your shins. Once you get to the aircraft, if a Jumpmaster does not tighten the Adjustable Leg Straps then, grab their attention and have them do it.

5. No opening shock. There is absolutely no reason for you to ever have to experience an opening shock when your parachute deploys. There is also no good reason why you would need to tighten your parachute so tight that you are hunched over like Yoda to prevent an opening shock. Fortunately, it only took me a few jumps for me to learn this next trick. The reason for the opening shock is people do not know how to properly take the slack out of the Diagonal Backstraps. Here is how you do it.

1. Elongate the Diagonal Backstraps all the way to the Diagonal Backstrap Friction Adapters before you put on your parachute (Figure 8-1).

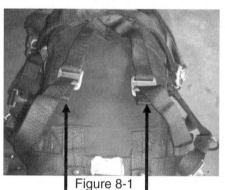

Figure 8-1
Elongated Diagonal Backstraps

2. Don your parachute and Aviator's Kit bag. Once you have adjusted your leg straps to where they are comfortable and put on your reserve parachute, it is time to adjust your Diagonal Backstraps.
3. Have your jump buddy (not rump buddy) stand behind you and grasp your Diagonal Backstraps on each side

just above your Leg Strap Ejector Snaps and pull the
Diagonal Backstraps out as far as he can (Figure 8-2).

Figure 8-2

4. (You) grasp the Diagonal Backstraps just above the Leg
    Strap Ejector Snaps and hold the Diagonal Backstraps
    tightly in place while your jump buddy now grasps the
    Diagonal Backstraps free-running ends at the edge of the
    Diagonal Backstrap Friction Adapters and pulls all the
    slack out in a seesaw motion (Figure 8-3).

Figure 8-3

5. Once all the slack is out, you can let go of the Diagonal Backstraps above the Leg Strap Ejector Snaps and instruct your jump buddy when the parachute harness feels COMFORTABLE. Once comfortable, your jump buddy S-folds the Diagonal Backstraps (Figure 8-4).

Figure 8-4

6. You have now successfully removed the slack in the Diagonal Backstraps that causes opening shocks. Continue donning your equipment in your normal manner. Note: Unless you weigh over 300 lbs or under 90lbs, you don't need to adjust the size of your parachute whether it is a size 2, 3, 4, or a size 5. It is the adjusting of the Diagonal Backstraps that prevents the opening shock and makes wearing a parachute as comfortable as wearing a parachute can be.

6. Parachute recovery. It never fails to amaze me how people never learn this trick. Once you have landed, placed your weapon into operation, and removed the parachute harness, it is now time to recover the parachute. Elongate the suspension

lines and when you get to the apex of the canopy where the Bridal Loop is, grasp the Bridal Loop (stick your right thumb through it) and move to where the <u>wind is blowing at your back</u> (The reason you move to where the wind is at your back is so the canopy can't catch any air) and then figure-eight roll the parachute and suspension lines back to the Aviator's Kit Bag. Once you place the parachute harness in the Aviator's Kit Bag, pull the Bridal Loop up out of the Aviator's Kit Bag with the hand that is still holding the Bridal Loop, route the waistband through the Bridal Loop, and snap the Aviator's Kit Bag up leaving 6-8" of the canopy and Bridal Loop exposed (out of the bag).

7. Pray. I always say a prayer for courage, competence, and safety before I jump and thank God for my blessings. Your life is on the line every time you jump; keep it real and go with God. What have you got to lose?

8. Watch. If you wear a watch, take if off and put it in a pocket somewhere because sooner or later it will be ripped off your wrist and it will be time to buy a new one. If you follow this tip alone, the purchase of this book was a sound investment.

9. Prerig equipment. Rig your ALICE Pack / MOLLE at least the day prior to your jump. That way you are not tooling around with it at the last minute and screwing something up.

10. See something wrong. If you notice something wrong inside or outside of the aircraft, notify a Jumpmaster immediately in a calm, professional way. You don't want to panic other jumpers and make the problem worse if you can help it.

11. Ear plugs. Always keep a pair with you in case the Air Force runs out. No need to become deaf any sooner than you need to.

12. Airborne (abn) school. Make sure you can run at least four miles in 34 minutes or less in warm weather and guys need to be able to do a minimum of 8 pull-ups. If you can't do both of these exercises to standard, you have no business going to Airborne school as you will be dropped from class, waste an Airborne slot, and waste the govt's money. Do us all a favor, get in shape! My book, "MAX Out the Army, Navy, and Marine Corps Fitness Test" will help you get in perfect shape for Airborne School.

13. Abn school. When you are doing Swing Lander Training (SLT), take a swig of water from your canteen in between every trip to the SLT. If you don't, you will become severely dehydrated in the GA heat.

CONCLUSION

I have presented you with many of the Jumpmaster secrets you need to know in order to become a successful Jumpmaster and be the best that you can be. Now, take this knowledge and put it to good use; our Soldiers deserve it! Also, always review the ASOP before conducting an ABN OP and when in doubt, ask for help.

ATW
CPT Kind

All glory is given to the Lord Jesus Christ for making this book possible. Philippians 4:16

Chp 9
BIOGRAPHY

CPT Lee A. Kind is a 1996 graduate of Augusta State University in Augusta, GA where he received a Bachelor of Business Administration Degree. He earned Distinguished Military Graduate honors and a Regular Army Commission as a Second Lieutenant in the Transportation Corps.

Upon graduation from the Transportation Officer Basic Course as the Distinguished Graduate, CPT Kind was assigned to the 82d Airborne Division for the next five years where he held the positions of: Platoon Leader, D/782d MSB (17 months); S2/3 Operations Officer, 782d MSB (21 months); Division Materiel Management Officer, DMMC (12 months), and Division Transportation Operations Officer (11 months). He then attended the Combined Logistics Officer Advanced Course. CPT Kind's next assignment was Commander, 584th Division Support Team (DST) for 2nd Infantry Division located at Camp Red Cloud, South Korea for 12 months and then he returned back to the 82d Airborne Division to serve as the Division Support Command S1.

CPT Kind's military education includes: Transportation Officer Basic Course, Combined Logistics Officer Advanced Course, CASQ, Automated Air Load Planning Course, Battalion Maintenance Officer Course, Airborne, Air Assault, and Jumpmaster schools.

CPT Kind's awards and decorations include the Bronze Star Medal, Meritorious Service Medal with one Oak Leaf Cluster, Army Commendation Medal with two Oak Leaf Clusters, Army Achievement Medal with four Oak Leaf Clusters, Global War on Terrorism Expeditionary and Service Medals, Korea Defense Service Medal, National Defense Service Medal w/ Bronze Star, Army Service Ribbon, Air Assault Badge, German Armed Forces Efficiency Badge in Gold, Venezuelan Parachutist Badge, Royal Thai Air Force Parachutist Badge, and the Master Parachutist Badge.

C-130: 2 Passes

SET UP AREA		R DOOR	L DOOR		SET UP AREA
FIRST OUTBOARD	FIRST INBOARD			FIRST INBOARD	FIRST OUTBOARD
LAST OUTBOARD	LAST INBOARD	MOCK DOOR		LAST INBOARD	LAST OUTBOARD

1. Set up
2. Static line class/SARJE
3. Set up
4. Move in to mock door
5. 2 passes (only 1st 23 jumpers get static line)
6. 1 pass (mass exit)
7. Set up
8. Move to pack shed

Jumpmasters Lead The Way!

C-130: 2 Passes

SET UP AREA			R DOOR	L DOOR		SET UP AREA	
O1	i4					i4	O1
-	-					-	-
O3	i23		MOCK DOOR			i23	O3
O24							O24
-							-
O31							O31

1. Set up
2. Static line class/SARJE
3. Set up
4. Move in to mock door
5. 2 passes (only 1st 23 jumpers get static line)
6. 1 pass (mass exit)
7. Set up
8. Move to pack shed

Jumpmasters Lead The Way!

51

C-130: 2 Passes

1. Jumpmasters sit with their stick in the a/c.

2. AJs will inspect the stick's leg straps prior to loading the a/c. PJ will oversee from the ramp.

3. AJs will lead the chalk out to the a/c. Safeties will control all other movements.

4. 30 second signal is a head nod from me for the final clear to the rear.

5. Safety duties in the mock up:

   a) DO NOT HAND OUT ANY STATIC LINES UNTIL EVERYONE IS SEATED and PJ says to. Note: Complete SARJE brief if not already done so.

   b) Hand out 1-3 outboard to the outboard and 5-23 inboard to the inboard. Leave back #4 inboard for the Jumpmasters.

   c) Adjust accordingly for the next pass. (O24-O31)

   d) Mass exit. Wait until everyone is seated. Hand out all outboard static lines to the #1 outboard and make the jumpers pass them back. Hand all inboard static lines -1 to the #1 inboard and make the jumpers pass back.

6. Safeties ensure outboard jumpers MOLLE/ALICE packs are on top of inboard jumpers MOLLE/ALICE packs in the a/c. (Seat inboard then the outboard jumper directly across from the inboard jumper)

7. Jumpers ALWAYS hook up where seated.

Jumpmasters Lead The Way!

APPENDIX A
Chart A-4

C-130: 3 Passes

SET UP AREA		
FIRST OUTBOARD	FIRST INBOARD	
LAST OUTBOARD	LAST INBOARD	

R DOOR	L DOOR
MOCK DOOR	

SET UP AREA	
FIRST INBOARD	FIRST OUTBOARD
LAST INBOARD	LAST OUTBOARD

1. Set up
2. Static line class/SARJE
3. Set up
4. Move in to mock door
5. 3 passes (only 1st 10 jumpers get static line)
6. 1 pass (mass exit)
7. Set up
8. Move to pack shed

Jumpmasters Lead The Way!

53

C-130: 3 Passes

SET UP AREA		R DOOR	L DOOR		SET UP AREA
O1	i4			i4	O1
-	-			-	-
O3	i23			i23	O3
O24		MOCK DOOR			O24
-					-
O31					O31

1. Set up
2. Static line class/SARJE
3. Set up
4. Move in to mock door
5. 3 passes (only 1st 10 jumpers get static line)
6. 1 pass (mass exit)
7. Set up
8. Move to pack shed

Jumpmasters Lead The Way!

C-130: 3 Passes

1. Jumpmasters sit with their stick in the a/c.

2. AJs will inspect their stick's leg straps prior to loading the a/c. PJ will oversee from the ramp.

3. AJs will lead the chalk out to the a/c. Safeties will control all other movements.

4. 30 second signal is a head nod from me for the final clear to the rear.

5. Safety duties in the mock up:

   a) DO NOT HAND OUT ANY STATIC LINES UNTIL EVERYONE IS SEATED and PJ says to. Note: Complete SARJE brief if not already done so.

   b) Hand out 1-3 outboard to the outboard and 9-10 inboard to the inboard. Leave back #4 inboard for the Jumpmasters.

   c) Adjust accordingly for the next two passes. (i11-i20, i21-i23 and O24-O31).

   d) Mass exit. Wait until everyone is seated. Hand out all outboard static lines to the #1 outboard and make the jumpers pass them back. Hand all inboard static lines -1 to the #1 inboard and make the jumpers pass back.

6. Safeties ensure outboard jumpers MOLLE/ALICE packs are on top of inboard jumpers MOLLE/ALICE packs in the a/c. (Seat inboard then the outboard jumper directly across from the inboard jumper)

7. Jumpers ALWAYS hook up where seated.

Jumpmasters Lead The Way!

C-17: 3 Passes

SET UP AREA				SET UP AREA	
FIRST OUTBOARD	FIRST INBOARD	R DOOR	L DOOR	FIRST INBOARD	FIRST OUTBOARD
LAST OUTBOARD	LAST INBOARD	MOCK DOOR		LAST INBOARD	LAST OUTBOARD

1. Set up
2. Static line class/SARJE
3. Set up
4. Move in to mock door
5. 3 passes* (only 1st 20 jumpers get static line)
6. 1 pass (mass exit)
7. Set up
8. Move to pack shed

* Exit 20, 20, 11

Jumpmasters Lead The Way!

56

C-17: 3 Passes

SET JP AREA		R DOOR	L DOOR		SET UP AREA	
O1	i28				i28	O1
-	-				-	-
O27	i51				i51	O27

MOCK DOOR

1. Set up
2. Static line class/SARJE
3. Set up
4. Move in to mock door
5. 3 passes* (only 1st 20 jumpers get static line)
6. 1 pass (mass exit)
7. Set up
8. Move to pack shed

* Exit 20, 20, 11

Jumpmasters Lead The Way!

C-17: 3 Passes

1. Jumpmasters sit with their stick in the a/c.
2. AJs will inspect their sticks leg straps prior to loading the a/c. PJ will oversee from the ramp.
3. AJs will lead the chalk out to the a/c. Safeties will control all other movements
4. Safety duties in the mock up:
   a) DO NOT HAND OUT ANY STATIC LINES UNTIL EVERYONE IS SEATED and PJ says to. Note: Complete SARJE brief if not already done so.
   b) Hand out 1-20 outboard to the outboard. Leave back #i28 for the jumpmaster. Safeties stand behind the inboard anchor line cable and sweep (take) static lines with the inboard hand, transition static line to outboard hand, and guide static line to top of the trail edge of the paratroop door until static line is taught.
   c) Adjust accordingly for next two passes. (O21-27 and i29-i41, i42-i51)
   d) Mass exit. Wait until everyone is seated. Hand out all outboard static lines to the #1 outboard and make the jumpers pass them back. Hand all inboard static lines -1 to the #1 inboard and make the jumpers pass them back
5. Jumpers ALWAYS hook up where seated.

Jumpmasters Lead The Way!

C17 – 2 Passes

SET UP AREA		R DOOR	L DOOR	SET UP AREA	
FIRST OUTBOARD	FIRST INBOARD			FIRST INBOARD	FIRST OUTBOARD
LAST OUTBOARD	LAST INBOARD	MOCK DOOR		LAST INBOARD	LAST OUTBOARD

1. Set up
2. Static line class/SARJE
3. Set up
4. Move in to mock door
5. 2 passes (only current pass gets static lines*)
6. 1 pass (mass exit)
7. Set up
8. Move to pack shed

* Exit 27, 24 (O1-O27 1st pass, i28-i51 2nd pass)

Jumpmasters Lead The Way!

C17 – 2 Passes

SET UP AREA	R DOOR	L DOOR	SET UP AREA	
O1	i28		i28	O1
-	-		-	-
O27	i51		i51	O27

MOCK DOOR

1. Set up
2. Static line class/SARJE
3. Set up
4. Move in to mock door
5. 2 passes (only current pass gets static lines*)
6. 1 pass (mass exit)
7. Set up
8. Move to pack shed

* Exit 27, 24 (O1-O27 1st pass, i28-i51 2nd pass)

Jumpmasters Lead The Way!

C17 – 2 Passes

1. Jumpmasters sit with their stick in the a/c.
2. AJs will inspect their sticks leg straps prior to loading the a/c. PJ will oversee from the ramp.
3. AJs will lead the chalk out to the a/c. Safeties will control all other movements
4. Safety duties in the mock up:
   a) DO NOT HAND OUT ANY STATIC LINES UNTIL EVERYONE IS SEATED and PJ says to. Note: Complete SARJE brief if not already done so.
   b) Hand out 1-27 outboard to the outboard. Leave back #28 for the jumpmaster. Safeties stand behind the inboard anchor line cable and sweep (take) static lines with the inboard hand, transition static line to outboard hand, and guide static line to top of the trail edge of the paratroop door until static line is taught.
   c) Adjust accordingly for the next pass(i28-i51).
   d) Mass exit. Wait until everyone is seated. Hand out all outboard static lines to the #1 outboard and make the jumpers pass them back. Hand all inboard static lines -1 to the #1 inboard and make the jumpers pass them back
5. Jumpers ALWAYS hook up where seated.

Jumpmasters Lead The Way!

61

APPENDIX B
AIRCRAFT INSPECTION CHECKLIST
(Checklist is not copyrighted)

1. ☐ Ensure Floors are
   - ☐ Clean
   - ☐ No excessive liquids on them
   - ☐ Non-skid material is present
2. ☐ Seats and Seatbelts are:
   - ☐ Configured correctly and enough*
     * Form X with all seatbelts to check and count
3. ☐ Excess AF equipment secured and out of way
4. ☐ BA-18 Parachutes present*
   * At least 2 for C-130 and 4 for C-141 and C-17s
5. ☐ Emergency Exits are outlined in yellow
6. ☐ Protruding sockets by doors are taped (C-130 and C-141)
7. ☐ U-bolts (sliver or green on C-130)
8. ☐ Anchor Line Cables*
   - ☐ No kinks
   - ☐ No rust
   - ☐ No frays
     * trace with 1/4 inch cotton webbing forward to aft
9. ☐ Static Line Retrieval System
   - ☐ Operational
   - ☐ 4" or higher above Anchor Line Cable
10. ☐ Paratroop Doors
    - ☐ No sharp or protruding edges
    - ☐ Pip-pin present and secured (C-130)
    - ☐ Manual lever for ramp secured (left door)
    - ☐ Troop Door Uplock (C-17)

APPENDIX B
AIRCRAFT INSPECTION CHECKLIST
(Checklist is not copyrighted)

11. ☐ Jump Platforms
    - ☐ No cracks or bends
    - ☐ Non-skid material is present
    - ☐ Down lock will seat properly
    - ☐ Secured to floor
    - ☐ Lower troop door clearance fairing operational (C-17)
12. ☐ Air Deflector (C-130, C-17), Air Spoiler (C-141)
    - ☐ Operational
    - ☐ No sharp or protruding edges
13. ☐ Jump Caution Lights- Operational (normal and tactical)*
    * 7 sets C-130, 5 sets (vis) C-141, C-17 4 sets (vis)
14. ☐ Emergency Bell Horn- Operational
15. ☐ Emergency Equipment
    - ☐ First Aid Kit
    - ☐ Fire Extinguishers
    - ☐ Oxygen masks (C-141)
    - ☐ CGU/1B tie down straps (C-130)
    - ☐ Roller Bar (C-141)
    - ☐ Canadian Retrieval System (C-17)
16. ☐ Public Address System- Operational
17. ☐ Air Sickness Bags
18. ☐ Ear Plugs
19. ☐ Water
20. ☐ Air Conditioning/Heater
21. ☐ Ask Loadmaster about any known deficiencies on the a/c

Books and other items I have found useful in my career:

"MAX Out the Army, Navy, and Marine Corps Physical Fitness Test." Whether you are a dud or a stud already, this book teaches you how to correctly and safely perform the exercises and provides a proven training plan that will enable any Soldier to max the PT tests. Priced right too. Available at:

www.Rangerjoes.com

The Ranger Digest volumes I- IX for great tips, tricks, and ideas for uses of many military items. Check out Ranger Rick's web page at:

www.Therangerdigest.com

U.S. Army Uniform Guide. The easiest way to make sure you are wearing your ribbons, awards, and insignia properly on your uniform. Contact at:

Uniform Guide
125 Roleen Court
Vallejo, CA 94589

To keep your weapon from jamming in the desert or the jungle, use Militec lubricant. It is the best and will save Soldiers' lives. Contact at:

www.Militec.com

That is all for now. If you like my book, please recommend it to a friend. Have a good one and don't forget you can email me for more copies of my book at:

atw82d@yahoo.com

All the way, Airborne!